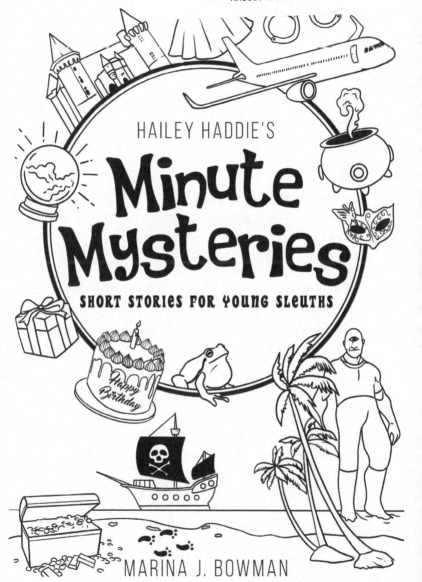

HAILEY HADDIE'S

Minute Mysteries

SHORT STORIES FOR YOUNG SLEUTHS

MARINA J. BOWMAN

First paperback edition June 2022

Written by Marina J. Bowman

ISBN 978-1-950341-50-4 (paperback)

ISBN 978-1-950341-51-1 (ebook)

Published by Code Pineapple

www.codepineapple.com

For aspiring amateur detectives -
you have been challenged!

Also By Marina J. Bowman

SCAREDY BAT
A supernatural detective series for kids with courage, teamwork, and problem solving.

#1 Scaredy Bat and the Frozen Vampires
#2 Scaredy Bat and the Sunscreen Snatcher
#3 Scaredy Bat and the Missing Jellyfish
#4 Scaredy Bat and the Haunted Movie Set
#5 Scaredy Bat and the Mega Park Mystery

THE LEGEND OF PINEAPPLE COVE
A mythical adventure series for kids with bravery, kindness, and friendship.

#1 Poseidon's Storm Blaster
#2 A Mermaid's Promise
#3 King of the Sea
#4 Protector's Pledge

Contents

Foreword   X

Detective's Note   XII

1. The Case of the   I
   Pilfering Pirates

2. The Case of the   6
   Confused Criminal

3. The Case of the   II
   Mystic Misfortune

4. The Case of the   15
   Cake Catastrophe

5. The Case of the   20
   Potion Poacher

6. The Case of the   25
    Baffling Boat Bet

7. The Case of the   30
    Vexing Vacation

8. The Case of the   35
    Stolen Stones

9. The Case of the   40
    Wandering Watch

10. The Case of the   45
    Clever Kidnapper

11. The Case of the   49
    Troubled Trial

12. The Case of the   54
    Cafeteria Crook

13. The Case of the   58
    Suspect Sorcerer

14. The Case of the   63
    Bathtime Bother

15. The Case of the   68
    Leaping Laboratory

IT STANDS TO REASON   73
A Mystery Game

MYSTERIES SOLVED   75

Mystery-Solving Tips   94

Discussion Questions   96

About the Author   98

Foreword

Solving criminal mysteries is one of the most intriguing forms of mental activity. Beyond intelligence and reasoning ability, it also requires perception, intuition, and a natural understanding of human behavior. Furthermore, some knowledge of the mythical or magical is helpful.

Ms. Haddie's well thought-out series of mysteries might be said to represent a fair sampling of the problems confronting the crime-solvers of the nation. The points of evidence are cleverly assembled and the various ways the culprits are revealed is skillfully done.

Readers interested in solving these problems should seek to think not only as a detective but as the criminal in the case would too. For example, what was their motivation? What were they trying to accomplish?

In this fresh challenge to junior detectives, Ms. Haddie offers an excellent opportunity—that of examining and forming conclusions about the more elemental, vital, and dramatic aspects of this thing called crime.

- Lewis E. Lawes

Detective's Note

From small cafeteria crimes to big jewel heists, I love to solve all mysteries! I may be known as the famous Hailey Haddie nowadays, but once upon a time I was just a young vampire detective with big dreams. Perhaps you even heard about me from junior crime solver Ellie "Scaredy Bat" Spark.

In the following pages, you will find some interesting experiences taken from my case book.

In these accounts, every fact, every clue necessary to the solution is given. The answer is in the story itself. You need look nowhere else. Each problem has only one solution.

Written in three hundred words or so, these short stories can be read in about a minute and solved in a few more.

I hope you will find them as enjoyable to read as they were to write.

Good luck, detective!

- Hailey Haddie

The Case of the

Pilfering Pirates

The cat clock on the wall meowed as Mrs. Rollins entered my office. It was five o'clock—she was right on time. The leather chair squeaked as she took a seat on the other side of my bright red desk.

I flipped open my tattered blue notepad. "Tell me exactly what happened," I said.

"It was a dark, moonless night at the marina," she began. "The wind was calm and the air was warm, so we anchored the boat to enjoy a delicious lobster dinner on deck. It was lovely until the candles burnt out and I could barely see right in front of me. So

I certainly didn't notice the pirate ship pull up beside us. However, around midnight, I could hear steps at the front of the boat, so my husband went to investigate. Soon after he left, I heard a parrot squawking, 'We're here for your gold. We're here for your gold!'" Mrs. Rollins wiped her teary eye with her fur sleeve. "I get chills just thinking about it."

"And then what?" I asked after jotting down some notes.

"I peeked from the back of the boat and saw a pirate with a silver skull pendant had captured my husband," she continued. "They demanded to know where the jewels were hidden, so my husband told them. And who could blame him? If he didn't, they threatened to make him walk the plank. Then a pirate with a dark blue bandana and gold tooth stole my jewels right from under the floorboard at the front of the ship." Mrs. Rollins whimpered and began to sob. "Soon, they saw me. A pirate that smelled like rotting fish tied us up. Then, they left with all the jewels!"

I handed her a tissue, and she blew her nose. "You might want to save those fake tears for the judge," I whispered to her. "I know you're lying."

How did I know Mrs. Rollins was lying?

HINT: Focus on the contradictions in Mrs. Rollins' story

SUPER HINT: Consider the five senses and their limitations

The solution is found on page 76

The Case of the
Confused Criminal

Brittany Hobbs' staticky brown hair stood on end as she dug through her metal trunk. She yanked out glass vials of mushrooms, gnome toenail clippings, dragon scales, and other magic ingredients. But there was no troll hair—the one thing she needed to make her magic spell work. Luckily, she knew a place nearby that kept such a rarity—Hilton Hill mansion.

Learning of the Witches Gala being held there, she dressed up in her best pink gown to sneak in. She stashed a thief's ski mask, gloves, and a canvas bag under her poofy dress and made her way to the mansion.

There was more security than she had imagined, but with her lavish dress and hairstyle with a hundred bobby pins that took her two hours to put together, she fit right in.

Soon she found the door that led to the witch's pantry where the troll hair was kept. She marked it in her memory and made her way outside. The night air was crisp and cool against her skin as she watched the party clear out from a nearby garden bench. After a large group of cackling witches flew off, she made her move. She climbed the drainpipe—quite an impressive feat wearing a dress—and snuck in through the window. Once inside, she slipped on her gloves and ski mask before making her way to the pantry.

There it was in all of its sparkling glory—troll hair! She stuffed the mason jar into her canvas bag, slipped off her gloves, and stashed them both under her dress. She made her way back down the drainpipe.

No sooner had she rounded the corner than a flashlight blinded her.

"Hey, what are you doing over there?" asked a short, stout security elf.

Brittany gave her best and most charming smile. "Hi there. Oh my, I think I got lost from the party. Can you help me get back?" She batted her eyelashes.

"I don't think so. You're going to have to come with me." The elf escorted Brittany to the security office and called the police.

"But I didn't do anything!" Brittany pleaded. The security guard rolled his bulgy eyes. "Yes, you look completely innocent."

Why did the security elf think Brittany was guilty?

HINT: Sometimes thieves are two-faced

SUPER HINT: Focus on what Brittany did right before and right after she grabbed the troll hair

The solution is found on page 77

The Case of the

Mystic Misfortune

The sweet scent of strawberry pie made my mouth water as I walked to Fitzgerald Bakery for lunch. It smelled so delicious I *almost* forgot about the odd case that had landed on my desk earlier that day.

I pulled out my notepad and re-read Juniper Jones' statement.

"I know it sounds fishy, but I was walking along Sixteenth Street, minding my business. When I walked in front of number 26, I heard an old fortune-teller scream, "My crystal ball! My crystal ball! They took my crystal ball!" I dashed up the front porch steps to the

house and pushed the door open. It swung in and punched a hole in the entryway's flowery wallpaper as I raced inside. I ran into a big guy with a burly beard and thick glasses halfway through the hall and thought he might be mad about the wall. Instead, he smiled at me and said, 'Ah, just in time!' I asked him what was going on, but he didn't reply.

It wasn't long before a policeman arrested me, along with the big guy and some woman. Neither one of them would talk to me on the way out, so I don't know what happened. Not only have the police clearly arrested the wrong person, but they almost pushed the front door into my face as I was standing on the front porch. I don't know what happened to the crystal ball, but I do know I'm innocent. Hailey, you have to help me!"

I gasped, turned around, and raced back to the office. A detail was wrong in Juniper's story. Strawberry pie would have to wait!

What is the inconsistent detail in the story?

HINT: Finding a hole in the details will blow this case wide open

SUPER HINT: Consider Juniper's experience as she enters and exits the crime scene

The solution is found on page 78

The Case of the
Cake Catastrophe

Two sisters fidgeted around a kitchen table in a stuffy farmhouse kitchen. Emily rubbed blue icing off her finger as she told me the story.

"My mom hurried into my bedroom," she explained. "She told me she forgot candles for my brother's birthday, so she was going to get some. She asked me to take his birthday cake out of the freezer. I was busy braiding my hair, so I sent Tracy to take the cake out. A few minutes later, I heard a scream and rushed downstairs."

"Okay, then what happened?" I turned to Tracy, who was sitting on the other side of the table.

"I went to the kitchen but stopped before entering, thinking I heard a noise. Someone was moving around, but who? Mom was out, and everyone else was upstairs. So, I carefully opened the door and found a raccoon eating the cake! It was ruined. The raccoon licked the blue and white icing clean off before dashing out the open window. He even ate all the dinosaur-shaped candies on the top."

"Exactly what time was that?" I asked.

"Around three o'clock," Tracy answered.

"Had either of you been in the kitchen this morning?" I asked.

"No," Emily answered. "Mom was making the cake, and she never lets us see it before it's lit with candles."

"What happened next?" I asked.

"Well, Mom came home and was obviously really mad. Our brother cried because the cake was ruined," Emily said.

"Did either of you go grocery shopping with your mother this week?" I asked the sisters. They both shook their heads.

"That's what I thought," I said. "That means there was no raccoon and one of you ate the cake."

Which sister ate the cake?

HINT: The details you need to focus on are quite delicious

SUPER HINT: Consider what Tracy could reasonably have known and seen

The solution is found on page 79

The Case of the

Potion Poacher

Professor Lamper touched the glass jellyfish sitting on the metal shelf as I entered my office. As I walked past him, the fresh scent of clean laundry filled my nose.

"Sorry I'm late," I said. I looked over my notes once more and plopped down at my red desk to start our meeting. "You say that Robert, your butler, called for help. Then, as he did, a stranger named Jeff that was passing the castle rushed in?"

"That's right," Professor Lamper confirmed. He took a seat in the squeaky chair across from me. "It was rather late last Friday evening before I was ready to leave town for the weekend. As Robert wasn't feeling well, I locked up the castle when I left."

I scribbled a few notes in my notepad.

"I had some rare potions brewing, the kind that turn you into a cat, so Robert said he would keep an eye on them," Lamper continued. "After all, his living quarters are right down the hall. About eleven that night, he heard a humming noise and, having the potions in mind, ran to my lab to investigate.

Finding the cauldrons empty and the potions gone, he let out a scream for help."

"Do you trust Robert?" I asked.

Professor Lamper straightened his posture. "Why, yes. Robert has been with me for years, and I trust him one hundred percent."

"Did Jeff, the stranger, see anyone leave when he was outside?"

"No. The thief or thieves must have left by the back door, as Jeff was right in front of the castle when he heard Robert's call for help and ran inside," replied Lamper. "Both men say the room smelled of strong perfume, so the burglars must have just left."

"Was the back door unlocked?" I asked.

"No, it was closed. It has a device that locks it automatically from the outside when it's pulled shut."

"Well, you'd better go talk to Robert and Jeff," I said. "I'm sure they know where your potions are. Long service isn't necessarily a pledge of loyalty."

How did I know Robert and Jeff were responsible for the missing potions?

HINT: Focus on the actions of Jeff, the stranger

SUPER HINT: It is ironic that Robert and Jeff may be locked up for their actions considering the clue that gave them away

The solution is found on page 80

The Case of the

Baffling Boat Bet

A s a waiter walked by with a sizzling steak, my friend John's stomach grumbled. He tapped his fingers against the wood table impatiently.

"The food is always so slow here," he complained.

I agreed and pulled out my phone. "Here. Check this out to pass some time." I laughed as I showed him an email my friend Cecilia had sent me from California.

John read the following:

There was a big boat race this weekend and everyone was in town. Who could blame them, though? The grand prize was one thousand dollars! If I had enough motivation to build my own wooden boat, I would have entered—even if it is mostly kids that take part.

So, I'm sunbathing on the beach in my favorite polka-dot bikini; you know the one. And these three kids start complaining really loudly nearby. I'm trying to get some sun and listen to music, but their complaining is distracting. Finally, I ask them what they are so bummed about.

Apparently, the three of them had bet their best baseball cards that whichever of their three boats comes in last gets the cards. Weirdos. However, they obviously also want the prize money, but none of them want to lose their cards. I ask if they can just break the bet, but apparently, they spit on their hands and shook on it. Which I guess is binding in kid code. Who knew! So gross.

I nod, smile, and then turn over to get some sun on my back. Kids these days. But I'm trying to lie there and they keep yammering on. Finally, I whisper the same advice into each of their ears, and they all take off running. I ended up burning from not enough sunscreen, but the race was fun to watch!

"It is amusing," laughed John, "but Cecilia forgot to say what she whispered!"

A smirk stretched across my face. "There was a way that one kid could win the money *and* keep their baseball cards. Think about it."

What advice did Cecilia whisper to each of the kids?

HINT: Focus on the boats

SUPER HINT: Consider stepping into someone else's shoes

The solution is found on page 81

The Case of the
Vexing Vacation

I took a sip of my hot, sweet cherry tea and
smiled at the mail in my other hand. Ellie
Spark had sent me a postcard telling me all
about her latest adventure as a young vampire
detective. My mind wandered back a few
years ago when I was just a teenage detective.
I thought specifically about my friend Sally
before homecoming.

*"Why the rush to get back to New York?" I
asked, a few minutes after Sally stepped off her
plane. "I thought you intended to spend all
summer in Cuba." My flip-flops could hardly*

keep up with her as she whizzed through the loud, crowded airport.

"Well, I saw on social media that Kylie is running for homecoming queen this fall. I can't let her win, so I need to start campaigning now. Look at this." She scrolled to a post from June 25th, just yesterday.

We walked through the airport gift shop as Sally looked for souvenirs to bring her friends. She held up a pink shirt. "Too bright?" She quickly put it down and resumed searching.

"Kimberly told me about what she sent you," I said, ignoring the talk of souvenirs. "Are you sure you didn't come back because Kimberly sent you a letter that told you about Ryan and Lisa's breakup? After all, you did have a crush on Ryan last year."

"No way!" Sally shrieked. "I just don't want Kylie to win homecoming queen. Plus, my family's beach house in Cuba doesn't even get internet or a phone signal. It's like living in the dark ages! I'm pretty sure there is a VCR there with a tape of Bambi still stuck in it."

"Oh, that's a bummer," I said. "Why did your plane come from Florida?"

Sally shuffled. "Oh, um, our beach house is just really remote, so not a lot of planes fly out of there. Very exclusive. So, we had to connect to a Florida flight."

I shook my head as I thought about how suspicious Sally was that day.

Why were Sally's actions suspicious?

HINT: Focus on Sally's answers to the questions

SUPER HINT: Consider the limitations of Sally's family beach house

The solution is found on page 82

The Case of the

Stolen Stones

I scribbled down the time and date that the precious stones had been stolen from the science fair in my notebook: 12:30 p.m., 11/11/11. There were no fingerprints or clues anywhere at the scene of the crime.

"Found anything?" asked Mr. Lawson nervously as he entered the gym.

"Not yet. Are you the only one with access to the gym?"

"No. Miss Leoni also has a key."

"Where is she now?"

"Oh, she left about an hour ago for lunch."

At 1:40 p.m., I noticed Jones, the gardener, working at the edge of a flower bed outside the school. He kept looking at the door while he frantically covered the hole he had dug. Finishing, he rushed toward the back of the building.

I followed Jones and reached the parking lot just as Miss Leoni pulled in.

"Having a nice day?" I asked.

"Of course. The weather is so lovely," Miss Leoni replied.

"Where were you when the precious stones went missing from the science fair?"

"Oh, no! Something went missing at the science fair?"

I repeated myself. "Where were you at the time of the robbery, 12:30?"

"I was shopping, of course! Don't you know that the mall is having a huge sale today?" She pointed to the pink shopping bags in her backseat. "I had to skip my lunch, but it was worth it!" She showed me a receipt that said 12:30 p.m., 11/1/11.

"What did you buy?"

"I got some sandals, a few pairs of shorts, a straw hat, and this super cute scarf." The excitement on Miss Leoni's face soon disappeared. "Is Mr. Lawson accusing me? You know, I can see him being a thief. He's always so secretive."

"No, Mr. Lawson isn't accusing you. But I am!"

Why did I suspect Miss Leoni?

HINT: What could have saved Miss Leoni ended up being her downfall

SUPER HINT: Focus on Miss Leoni's supposed alibi

The solution is found on page 83

The Case of the

Wandering Watch

Gabe sobbed and blew his nose into his sleeve. I gagged as globs of green boogers gunked up the fleece fabric. Not even the comforting smell of the nearby flowers soothed my churning stomach.

"That watch was priceless and belonged to my grandfather! It was encrusted with dozens of diamonds. What will I do?" he asked.

I turned my attention to the ground beneath the bedroom window. It was 6:00 a.m., earlier than I usually start a case, but crime doesn't wait.

"I was restless all night," said Gabe as I knelt beside a deep impression of a man's right shoe.

I gave a small grunt. "Darn, I thought the raindrops on that leaf in the footprint were one of those diamonds." I admired the way the light reflected off the droplets sitting atop the orange leaf.

"It was actually the rain that woke me up this morning," said Gabe. "It only lasted about fifteen minutes. I dozed off again and awakened with a fright. I saw a man jump to the ground from my bedroom window."

"Was that just before you called me?" I asked.

"Yes." Gabe nodded.

"Are you alone at the house?"

Gabe nodded once more. "I can't believe the watch is gone!" he cried. A snot bubble blew from his nostril and promptly popped.

"Do you know anyone who chews blue bubblegum?" I asked as I poked a piece nearby with a stick.

"Yes. Tina, who brought me home last night. However, I threw that one there."

I looked at the window. "Looks like the thief chiseled open this window directly under your bedroom."

"I wondered how he got in! The doors were all locked," explained Gabe.

I sighed. "I have another case to attend to, so let's get this over with. I know that watch was heavily insured and I also know that you need money for a new car. You faked the robbery. Who helped you? Was it Tina?"

What clue led me to this conclusion?

HINT: Focus on the inconsistency in the timeline of events that Gabe described

SUPER HINT: Consider the physical details that the detective noticed

The solution is found on page 84

The Case of the
Clever Kidnapper

I cracked open my office window. A cool breeze rustled the mess of paper strewn across my desk.

"Sometimes criminals are quite clever," I scribbled in my journal log. "In fact, one of the most interesting cases I've come across happened just last week."

"A girl's teddy bear was kidnapped from the playground, and she called me. When I arrived, I searched and found no clues. I felt bad that there wasn't much I could do, but soon, after hours of tears, a box with no return address arrived on her doorstep. It shook slightly as it sat there. The girl ripped open the box to find a note, as well as a way to give the criminal his or her demands."

The note said:

I require 2 homemade cookies and 1 lollipop. Then you can have your teddy back. Send it by dinnertime tonight. No later than 7 o'clock.

"The girl did as she was told, and her teddy showed up on her doorstep safe and sound. But how did the kidnappers get away with it without having their whereabouts discovered?"

How did the kidnappers get away with it?

HINT: Focus on what was inside the box

SUPER HINT: Consider what would allow the girl to mail the demands to the kidnappers without using a return address

The solution is found on page 85

The Case of the

Troubled Trial

I popped a stick of bubblegum in my mouth as I took my seat in court. I could hardly sit still. After all, it's not every day a dragon tries to sue a train for damages!

A cyclops sat on the witness stand with a thump, his large eye peering into the crowd. He muttered something in Cyclopian, but I didn't understand until the interpreter translated.

"The witness says the train conductor in the blue hat yelled for him to 'Stop right there and show me your identification!'" explained the interpreter. "So he did. They checked his ID thoroughly. They didn't seem very friendly to foreigners."

The cyclops' lip trembled as his words were translated.

"He further says that there were two vampires on the train car and that they jumped off and ran away."

"Have they been located yet?" inquired the judge.

"No, Your Honor; we've been unable to trace them, although the conductor gave a good description," replied counsel.

The interpreter continued, "The witness declares he had a clear view of the dragon when he got off the train. He states that just as the dragon put his foot on the ground, the train suddenly started and he was thrown to the road."

"Can't the witness understand or speak enough English to tell the court about that himself?" asked the judge.

"No, Your Honor. He's only been in this country for two weeks. The only English words he knows are 'hello' and 'thank you.'"

"How can he ride the train alone then?"

"Some friends put him on the train and called his family to meet him at the end of the line," replied counsel.

"Continue."

"Cyclops," declared the interpreter, "says he picked up this picture from the floor of the car—a snapshot of a vampire and a girl."

"Case dismissed," thundered the judge. "And don't ever bring another case like this into my court again."

Why was His Honor justified in dismissing the dragon's case?

HINT: Focus on the Cyclops' limitations as a witness

SUPER HINT: Consider the difference between the Cyclops' capability when he was riding the train and when he was in the courtroom

The solution is found on page 86

The Case of the

Cafeteria Crook

The smell of greasy fries lingered in the air. I held my magnifying glass up to the note left behind after all the cafeteria's salad went missing. "Even the smartest criminals leave clues," I said to the lunch lady. "Even if they're careful, they tend to leave some mark or clue behind."

She was too busy scooping pudding from a vat to say much, but she gave me a small nod. I put down my magnifying glass, noticing the note was an odd one—the criminal had signed their name. Even though the name belonged to a second grader, could they be so silly?

The note said:

I told u if u dn't bring back peeza mundays, I wood steel the salad. Breng back the pizza!

Yurs truly,
Jamie Williams

"Did someone threaten to steal the salad before?" I asked as I read the note.

The cafeteria lady shrugged. "I'm not sure. I'm new here. But it looks like it was Jamie Williams. Look, he signed the note and everything."

I smiled and shook my head. "It definitely wasn't Jamie; it was someone in a higher grade." After explaining why to the cafeteria lady, she agreed.

Examining the note more closely, I noticed all of the Ps in the note had a swirly swoop. I scanned the artwork lining the hallway done by kids in the fifth and sixth grades. Scott Peter had signed his hamster ninja portrait with the same type of P.

"Ah-ha! Got the salad thief!"

How did I know it had to be someone in a higher grade?

HINT: Focus on the note that was left behind

SUPER HINT: Consider the inconsistencies in the way the note was written

The solution is found on page 87

The Case of the

Suspect Sorcerer

The sorcerer jumped to his feet, knocking down the chair behind him. It fell on my office rug with a thump.

"Having these skeleton keys in my possession isn't proof that I had any part in the Smith robbery!" he exclaimed.

"I know all about your story," I said. "Now sit back down." He picked up the squeaky leather chair and adjusted his cape before taking a seat. I flipped open my notes.

"You said you found the keys yesterday at two p.m. in the lake, tied up in a white bag, didn't you? But what were you doing out in an open boat in the rainstorm that lasted all yesterday afternoon?"

"It was because of the rain that I went out," explained the sorcerer confidently. "Don't you know some spells need to be done in the rain to work? After trying to turn beetles into turtles for hours, I had rowed back to within a few yards of shore when I just happened to notice the bag lying on the bottom of the lake. So, I landed, tipped my boat over to keep the rain out, and waded in. The water at that point was over my waist and cold."

"Let's take a field trip," I said. After a short, tense car ride, we pulled up to the rickety old dock.

"On which side of the dock did you find the keys?" I asked.

The sorcerer pointed to the sandy bottom on the left.

"Think I'll talk with the mermaids," I said as I hopped into a docked boat.

I rowed like mad for about fifty yards and suddenly dropped the oars. After looking at the crystal-clear water to the bottom of the boat, I laughed.

"Silly of me not to have thought of that before," I thought. "Wonder if the sorcerer is better at magic than he is at lying."

How did I know the sorcerer was not telling the truth?

HINT: Focus on where the keys were supposedly found

SUPER HINT: Consider the conditions in which the sorcerer supposedly came across the keys

The solution is found on page 88

The Case of the

Bathtime Bother

I was sitting with my detective friend Colin in a café on a cozy autumn day. As we ate sweet biscuits and sipped hot mint tea, we shared stories.

"You've heard me talk about my eccentric friend Tom Sweden, haven't you?" Colin asked.

I nodded. "Very interesting guy. I hear his top-floor penthouse apartment is quite odd! But, of course, Tom never cared much about what people think, so I'm not surprised. I have yet to see it for myself."

Colin's eyes lit up. "Well then, do I have a story for you! Tom's place has six baths, but he loves to use the biggest one most of all. It is a large, all-tile bath, eighteen feet long, fifteen wide, and seven high. And none of his baths have a single window!" He sipped his mint tea before continuing.

"A few days ago, he went in the bath, locked the door, and turned the cold water on. When he went to turn it off, he found to his dismay that the mechanism controlling the drain and the taps wasn't working. He couldn't let the water out, and he couldn't turn the tap off. Nor could he unlock the door. He tried shouting, but no one could hear him. So there he was in a locked bath with no window. He couldn't open or break down the door, couldn't let the water out or turn it off. And he had no way of attracting attention."

"Is this going where I think it is?" I chuckled.

"This situation might have disturbed most people, but not Tom," Colin continued. "He leisurely proceeded with his bath and, when finished, casually left."

I laughed, almost shooting tea out of my nose. "That sounds like exactly what Tom would do. I don't think eccentric is a strong enough word for him! After all, there was only one way out."

How did Tom get out?

HINT: Focus on the specific words used to describe the scenario

SUPER HINT: Consider thinking outside the box

The solution is found on page 89

The Case of the

Leaping Laboratory

Ring! Ring! I glanced at my office's cat clock as I picked up my phone —10:15 a.m.

"Hello! Hailey?" came an agitated voice at the other end. "This is Dr. Sam Waters. Can you come over right away? Something has just happened, and I need your help."

"I'll be right there!" I said, springing from my chair. "Give me twenty minutes." As I drove my car down the winding dirt road to get to the lab, I thought about the wedding that I had just seen Dr. Waters at last weekend. We'd spent the night dancing, singing, and laughing. He even let me have his cake since he doesn't eat sugar. I wondered what could be so wrong a week later.

I parked at a brick building with smoke funneling from the top at 10:35 a.m. After one knock on the yellow door wedged under the blinking "Water's Lab" sign, a man with a broken tooth answered.

"Thank goodness you're here!" said the assistant. "Dr. Waters has turned into a frog— come quickly to the Potions Lab!"

I hurried to the room that reeked of lemons and found Dr. Waters hopping around the room, a croak coming from his throat.

"Oh no!" I cried. "What happened?" I watched Dr. Waters hop across a counter and shatter a beaker. Beside the glass on the floor was a half-eaten lollipop.

"I came in about an hour ago and went right to the Laser Lab to do some work. Twenty-five minutes ago, I came down and heard him talking on the phone as I passed the Potions Lab on my way to the kitchen for a piece of chocolate cake. I was there for about thirty minutes, I imagine. When I came back through the hall, I happened to look in here, and there he was just hopping around. I think he ate one of those lollipops and it turned him into a frog," he concluded.

I shook my head. "I don't know how this happened, but I know it wasn't the lollipop."

How did I know it wasn't the lollipop?

HINT: Consider Hailey's experience with Dr. Waters at the wedding

SUPER HINT: The answer is rather sweet

The solution is found on page 90

IT STANDS TO REASON

A Mystery Game

Here is a fun game of wits for a party of any size. It can be played in either of two ways:

1. Select one or more stories from the Minute Mysteries that sound interesting. Make as many copies of each as there are guests at the party. Then pass the copies around and allow a few minutes for your guests to study them. At the end of this time, each must hand you a written solution with the reasoning behind it. Compare these with the solutions at the back of the book; the one who is most often correct is the winner!

2. Instead of making copies of each story, you may read it aloud, slowly and carefully. It may be read a second time, if necessary. But after this, no questions may be asked. After the time limit has passed, each guest writes out their solution as in (1), and hands it to you for comparison with the solutions at the back of the book.

Method number one puts the emphasis on one's powers of reasoning and analysis; method number two adds to these a focus on an accurate memory. Let the games begin!

MYSTERIES SOLVED

1. PILFERING PIRATES

It would have been impossible for Mrs. Rollins to have seen so much detail about the pirates from the back of the ship. After all, it was a dark, moonless night. She said she could hardly see right in front of her—let alone all the way to the front of the ship.

2. CONFUSED CRIMINAL

Brittany forgot to remove her ski mask when she put away her gloves and the troll hair. So when security saw her, she looked suspiciously like she had been trying to break in and steal something—which is exactly what she was doing!

3. MYSTIC MISFORTUNE

Juniper said she pushed open the door when she rushed into the house. Yet the policeman pushed the door to go out of the house. The door only opens one way.

4. CAKE CATASTROPHE

Tracy licked off the icing! She wouldn't have known the details of the cake unless she had seen it earlier that morning or had been on the shopping trip for ingredients. Especially since the supposed "raccoon" ate the icing and dinosaur-shaped candies "clean off."

Emily may have seemed like the obvious choice since she had blue icing on her hand; however, there may be a cupcake wrapper in the garbage that could explain it.

5. POTION POACHER

The butler said that as he called for help, Jeff, a stranger, rushed in. Lamper had locked up before leaving and, therefore, Jeff could not have rushed in through a locked door. Robert and Jeff had to have been working together.

6. BAFFLING BOAT BET

She told them to "drive someone else's boat." By doing so, there was a chance one boy could win the prize by coming in first with another kid's boat, while also getting all the baseball cards if his own boat came in last.

7. VEXING VACATION

Sally said she came back because she didn't want to lose homecoming queen to Kylie, but Kylie had only announced she was running the day before. Plus, how would Sally have seen that post if she had no internet or phone signal in Cuba? With her being in such a remote part of Cuba with spotty flights, it is far more likely she came back because of Ryan.

8. STOLEN STONES

Miss Leoni had a shopping receipt for the wrong day. The crime took place at 12:30, 11/11/11, but her receipt was for the same time on a different day: 12:30, 11/1/11. So her alibi did not hold up.

9. WANDERING WATCH

The raindrops glistening on a leaf in the shoe impression. According to Gabe's statement, the burglar had jumped from the window *after* it had stopped raining.

10. CLEVER KIDNAPPER

A large carrier pigeon was inside the box. That way no return address was needed.

11. TROUBLED TRIAL

The cyclops witness could not understand or speak enough English to make a simple statement to the court. Yet he knew exactly what the conductor yelled at him when he was asked to stop and show his ID. This was so improbable that the judge dismissed the case.

12. CAFETERIA CROOK

The note, although misspelled like a second grader might, had perfect punctuation that only someone in a higher grade could do. Plus, "pizza" was spelled two very different ways, hinting that the misspellings were on purpose and Jamie Williams was framed.

13. SUSPECT SORCERER

The sorcerer could not have seen the bag on the bottom of the lake during a rainstorm. Even crystal-clear water in a rainstorm would have so much surface disturbance that an object on the bottom could not be seen.

14. BATHTIME BOTHER

You remember how Tom was eccentric? No mention of a bathroom was made, just a bath. His bath had no top, so he climbed out!

15. LEAPING LABORATORY

While it's true there was a half-eaten lollipop on the floor, Dr. Waters couldn't have been the one who ate it. Dr. Waters doesn't eat sugar. That was why Dr. Waters let Hailey Haddie have his cake at the wedding they attended together. It's more likely that the assistant was the one responsible for the half-eaten lollipop, since he clearly has a sweet tooth. It's the little things that count in crime detection.

Want to sharpen your detective skills?

New Step-By-Step Guide to Solving Mysteries

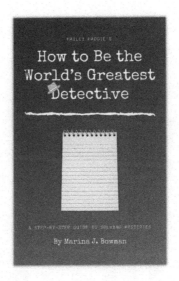

Learn how to become the world's greatest detective from the great Hailey Haddie!

Be first to know when it's released!
Visit <u>scaredybat.com/mm-guide</u>

WHAT'S NEXT

Did you enjoy the short mystery stories?
Then you'll love these full-length books!

Scaredy Bat: A Vampire Detective Series

Save 30% when you get the 3-book bundle!
Visit scaredybat.com/mm-bundle

Save 10% on the first book

Scaredy Bat and the Frozen Vampires

All of the guests at the royal vampire wedding are frozen solid! And if the wedding doesn't happen in time, Ellie's life will change forever.

Can Ellie face her fear and solve the mystery?

Save 10% at <u>scaredybat.com/mm-one</u>

Mystery-Solving Tips

Some of these mysteries involve a 'crime' and a 'culprit.' Use the below prompts to take notes as you read and solve each mystery!

Name: Write the name of the suspect, witness, or victim

Motive: Write the reason why a suspect might have committed the 'crime'

Access: Write the time and place it happened

How: Write the way the suspect could have committed the 'crime'

Clues: Write any observations or details that may support the motive, access, or how

Get the Suspect Template at:

scaredybat.com/mm-template

Discussion Questions

1. What did you enjoy about these minute mystery stories?

2. Which story was your favorite and why?

3. What are some of the story themes?

4. Were you able to solve the mysteries? If so, how?

5. Detective Superpowers: Would you rather have photographic memory or encyclopedic knowledge?

6. What other books, shows, or movies do these stories remind you of?

7. If you could talk to the author, what is one question you would ask her?

Dear Reader,

Hello there! Did you enjoy these short mystery stories? I know I did!

If you want to join the team as we solve more mysteries, then leave a review!

Otherwise, we won't know if you're up for the next case. And when we go to solve it, you may never hear about it!

You can leave a review wherever you found the book.

I'm excited to see you for the next mystery adventure!

Fingers crossed it's a super interesting one...

Yours Truly,

Detective Hailey Haddie

About the Author

MARINA J. BOWMAN is a writer and explorer who travels the world searching for wildly fantastical stories to share with her readers. Ever since she was a child, she has been fascinated with uncovering long lost secrets and chasing the mythical, magical, and supernatural. For her current story, Marina is investigating a charming town in the northern US, where vampires and humans live in harmony.

Marina enjoys sailing, flying, and nearly all other forms of transportation. She never strays far from the ocean for long, as it brings her both inspiration and peace. She stays away from the spotlight to maintain privacy and ensure the more unpleasant secrets she uncovers don't catch up with her.

As a matter of survival, Marina nearly always communicates with the public through her representative, Devin Cowick. Ms. Cowick is an entrepreneur who shares Marina's passion for travel and creative storytelling and is the co-founder of Code Pineapple.